Hwyl gyda Twts

Fun with Twts

Chris Glynn

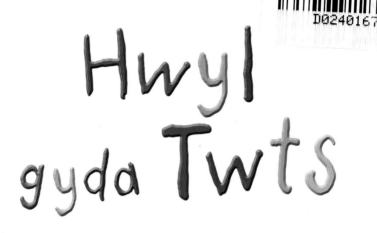

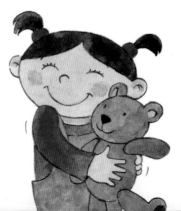

darllen

reading

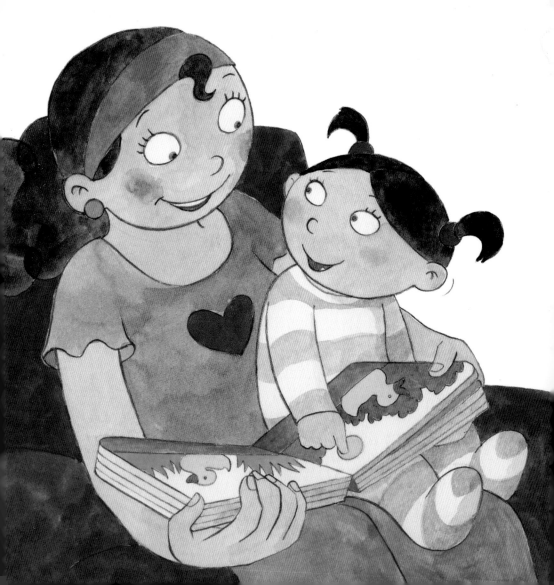

cadw sŵn

making a noise

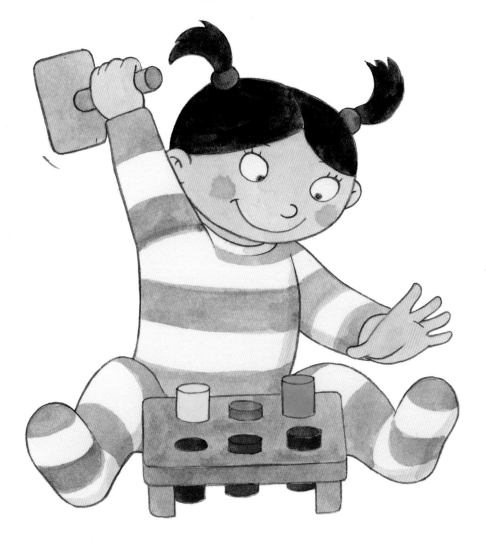

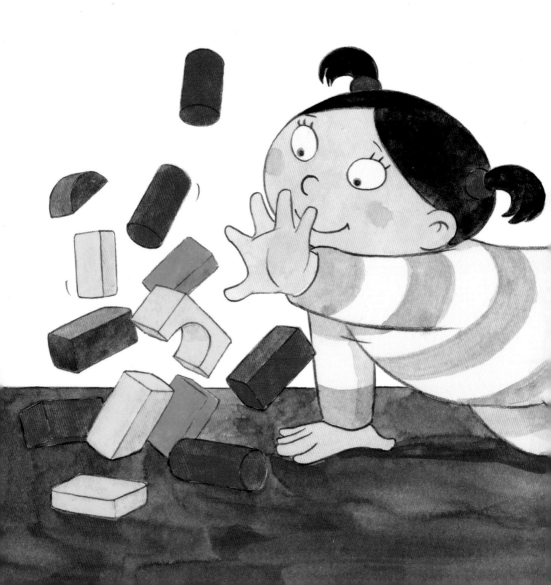

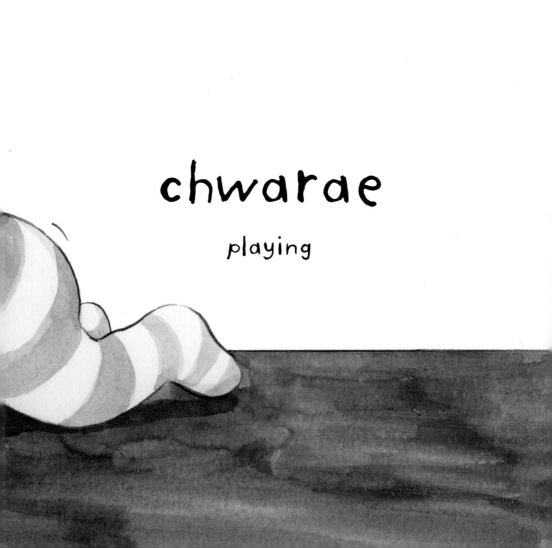

chwarae

playing

edrych

looking

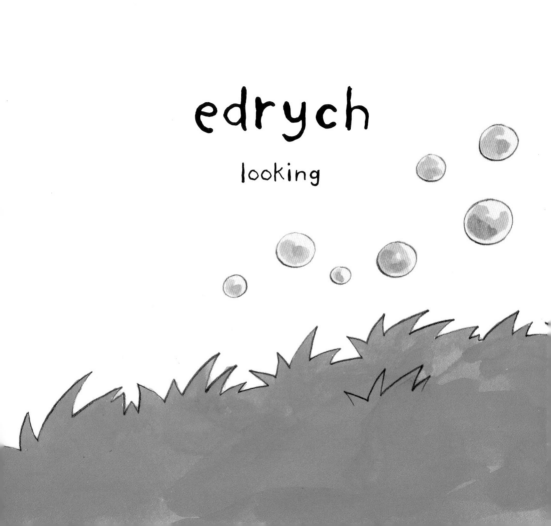

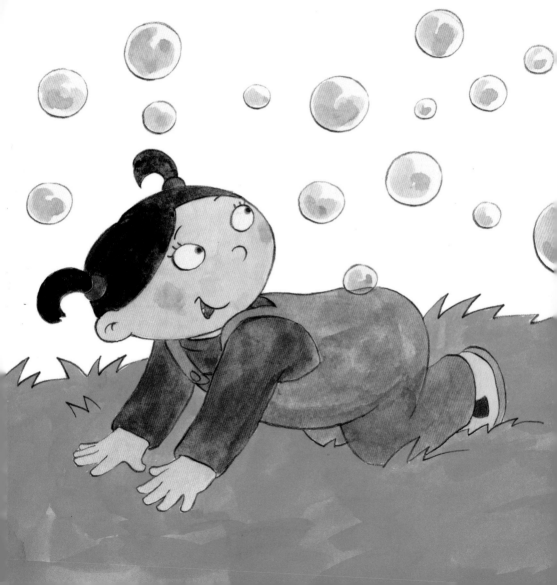

mynd am dro

going out and about

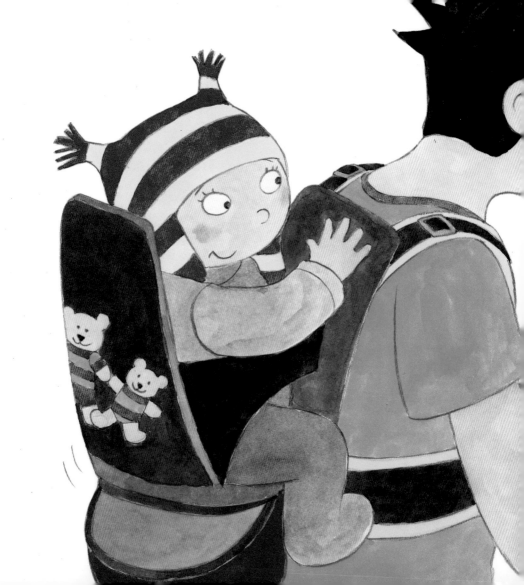

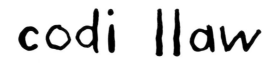

codi llaw

waving

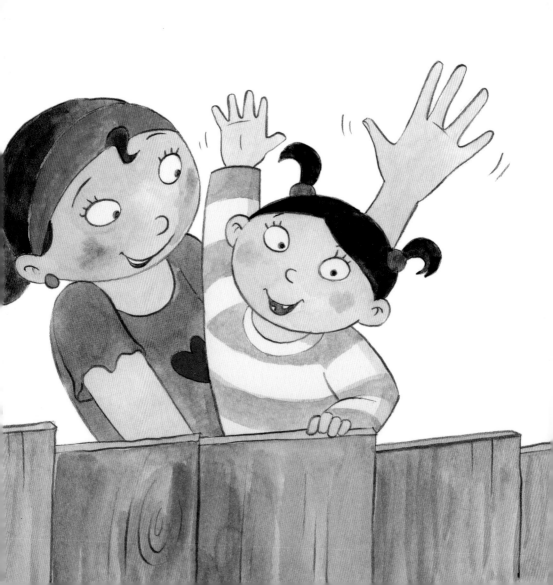

siopa

shopping

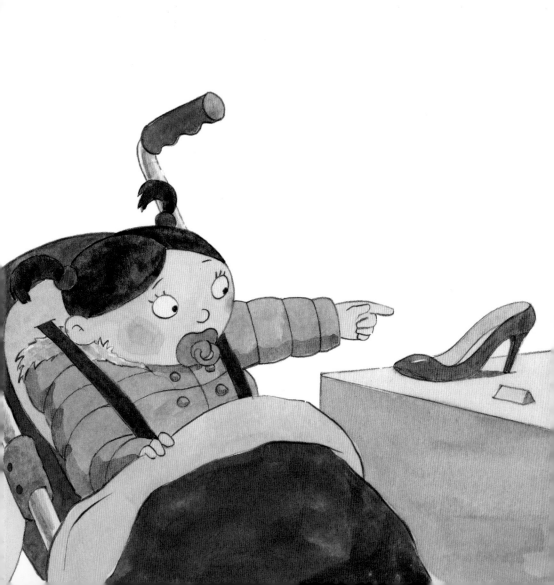

sblasio

splashing

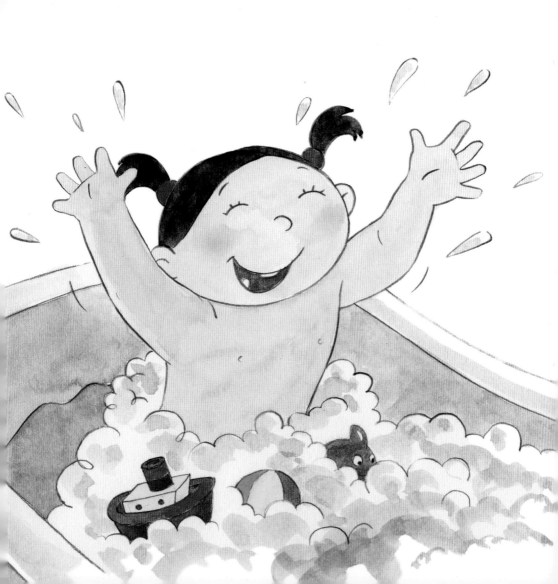

cwtsho

cuddling

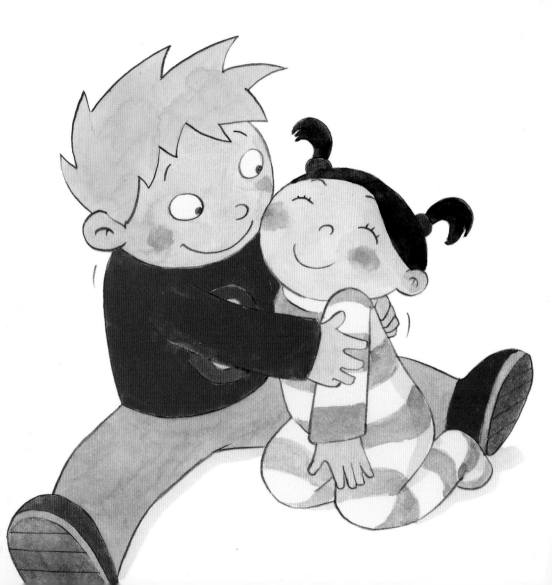

cysgu

sleeping

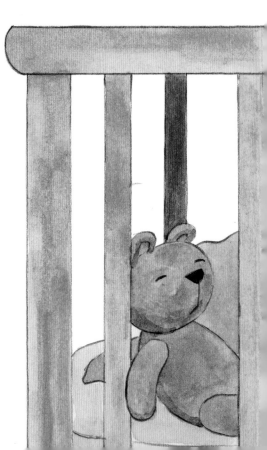